Maths Notebook

by Paul Forte
M.A. (Oxon), P.G.C.E.

Paul Forte has been teaching prep school maths for 25 years. He is an ISI inspector and regularly inspects maths departments around the country. He also sets problems for the Mathematics Association publication, Mathematical Pie, and is a former question setter for the ISEB 13+ Common Entrance maths papers.

This Maths Notebook is to be used as an aid to revision for Common Entrance and Scholarship examinations. It contains examples and step-by-step methods to solve common questions and summarises important methods. It is therefore intended that it be used for revision rather than as a text book. Key words have been <u>underlined</u> and students should try to learn their meanings and spellings.

Published by Paul Forte in 2011

Email: mathsnotebook@btinternet.com

ISBN   978-0-9554938-0-5

Priority Rules of Arithmetic

Some operations are more important than others, eg × is more important than +.

Some operations are as important as others, eg + is as important as -.

There are four levels of importance:

Brackets take priority over any operation

1. **Brackets**.

2. **Powers** and **square roots**.

3. **Multiply**, **divide**, **of**.

4. **Add**, **subtract**.

$\sqrt{}, \mathbf{x^n}$

$\mathbf{x}, \div$

$+, \cdot$

Here are some examples showing how to use these rules:

a) $5 + 3 \times 2 = 5 + 6 = 11$ *Do the 3 × 2 first as × is more important than +.*

b) $(5 + 3) \times 2 = 8 \times 2 = 16$ *Do whatever is in brackets first.*

c) $6 - 4 + 2 = 2 + 2 = 4$ *All at same level, so calculate from left to right.*

d) $6 - (4 + 2) = 6 - 6 = 0$ *Do whatever is in brackets first.*

2 *A Word Or Two About Numbers*

The Four Rules

In <u>addition</u>, the answer is called the <u>SUM</u>.
In <u>subtraction</u>, it is called the <u>DIFFERENCE</u>.

In <u>multiplication</u>, the answer is the <u>PRODUCT</u>.
In <u>division</u>, the answer is called the <u>QUOTIENT</u>.

Squares and Cubes

Dividing a number by three is not the same as cube rooting it

A <u>SQUARE</u> number, or a <u>perfect square</u>, is a whole number that results from multiplying a number by itself.
So 64 is a square number because 8 x 8 = 64.

The <u>SQUARE ROOT</u> of a number is the number which when multiplied by itself gives you the original number.
So 6 is the square root of 36 because 36 = 6 x 6 or 6^2.
We write $\sqrt{36} = 6$.

Learn the first few perfect squares:
**1   4   9   16   25   36   49
64   81   100 121 144.....**

A <u>CUBE</u> number or a <u>perfect cube</u> is a whole number that results from multiplying a number by itself and then by itself again.
So 8 is a cube number because 2 x 2 x 2 = 8

The <u>CUBE ROOT</u> of a number is the number which when multiplied by itself and by itself again gives you the original number.
So 4 is the cube root of 64 because 64 = 4 x 4 x 4 or 4^3.
We write $_3\sqrt{64} = 4$.

Learn the first few cube numbers: **1   8   27   64   125   216....**

Factors, multiples and prime numbers

A <u>FACTOR</u> of a whole number is a number which goes into it exactly without leaving a remainder.

So 3 is a factor of 12, because $12 \div 3 = 4$
But 7 is not a factor of 15 because $15 \div 7 = 2 \, r1$

A <u>PRIME NUMBER</u> or prime is a whole number which has no factors other than itself and 1. A prime number always has exactly two factors. The list of primes is neverending, but it starts like this:

2   3   5   7   11   13   17   19   23   29   31   37   41
43   47   53   59   61   67   71   73   79   83   89   97........

> **Remember that 1 is not counted as a prime number**

A <u>MULTIPLE</u> of a whole number is a number found in its times table.
So 12 is a multiple of 3, because $4 \times 3 = 12$ i.e. 12 is in the 3 times table.
But 15 is not a multiple of 7, because 15 is not in the 7 times table.

Multiples of 2 are called <u>EVEN</u> numbers.
Whole numbers which are not divisible by 2 are called <u>ODD</u>.

An <u>INTEGER</u> is a whole number
eg 3, 65, 1004, but not 34.5, 643.23.

Number Tricks

Opposites

We know that 6 x 4 = 24.

If we <u>halve</u> 6 and <u>double</u> 4,
we get 3 x 8 which is still 24.

If we <u>multiply</u> 6 by 10 and <u>divide</u> 4 by 10,
we get 60 x 0.4 = 24.

So <u>multiplying</u> and <u>dividing</u> are
opposites (inverses).

We know that 5 + 7 = 12.

If we <u>add</u> 3 to 5 and <u>subtract</u> 3 from 7, we get 8 + 4
which is still 12.

So <u>adding</u> and <u>subtracting</u> are also opposites (inverses).

A 3-way connection

There is a 3-way connection with numbers involving multiplication aand division.

Example $12 = 4 \times 3$ and so $4 = \dfrac{12}{3}$ and $3 = \dfrac{12}{4}$

This also works with decimals, fractions, negative numbers etc...

$$12 = 4 \times 3$$

$$4 = \frac{12}{3} \qquad\qquad 3 = \frac{12}{4}$$

Long Multiplication

When we work out 23 x 136 we work out 23 lots of 136.

To do this, we simply add together 3 lots of 136 and 20 lots of 136.

The sum is set out like this:

```
 136
  23
 408      this is 3 lots of 136
2720  +   this is 20 lots of 136 ie 2 lots of 136 with an extra 0 at the right hand end
3128      this is 3 lots of 136 + 20 lots of 136 ie 23 lots of 136
```

Multiplication and Division by factors

We can use factors to multiply and divide by larger numbers.

To multiply by 24, we could multiply by 3 and then multiply that answer by 8.

eg   16 x 24 = 16 x 3 x 8 = 48 x 8 = 384 } Same final answer even if you use
or   16 x 24 = 16 x 4 x 6 = 64 x 6 = 384 } different factors.

To divide by 24 we could divide by 3 and then divide that answer by 8.

```
        3 | 504
        8 | 168
            21
  or                   Same final answer even if you use
                       a different set of factors
        4 | 504
        6 | 126
            21
```

Will it divide?

It is often useful to be able to test whether a number like 10000 is divisible by say 3, without actually doing the division sum.

Here are the rules for testing by each number.

Dividing by	Rule	Example	Counterexample
1	All numbers are divisible by 1		
2	Number ends in 0, 2, 4, 6 or 8	24, 558, 10006	25, 557, 24687
3	Sum of digits is divisible by 3	57 because 5 + 7 = 12 which is divisible by 3	59 because 5 + 9 = 14 which is not divisible by 3
4	Last two digits divisible by 4	23512 because 12 is divisible by 4	24326 because 26 is not divisible by 4
5	Number ends in 0 or 5	25, 2340, 13400	34, 55554, 10009
6	Rules for 2 and 3 must both work	54 because it ends in a 4 and 5 + 4 = 9 which is divisible by 3	57 because it ends in a 7
7	No easy test available		
8	Last three digits divisible by 8	23408 because 408 is divisible by 8	88588 because 588 is not divisible by 8
9	Sum of digits is divisible by 9	3555 because 3 + 5 + 5 + 5 = 18 which is divisible by 9	2433 because 2 + 4 + 3 + 3 = 12 which is not divisible by 9
10	Number ends in a 0	20, 250, 2050, 6470	245, 60003, 5736
11	Digit sum of alternate numbers differs by 0 or a multiple of 11	265078 because 2 + 5 + 7 = 14 and 6 + 0 + 8 = 14 19261 because 1 + 2 + 1 = 4 and 9 + 6 = 15 which differ by 11	1234567 because 1 + 3 + 5 + 7 = 16 and 2 + 4 + 6 = 12 which do not differ by a multiple of 11
100	Number ends in 00	200, 53400	234, 2540, 100040
1000	Number ends in 000	3000, 32000	200, 534, 50300

Place Value

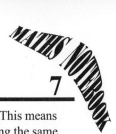

In our number system, the value of a number depends on where it is. This means that the 5 in 53 is worth more than the 5 in 35 even though we are using the same digit 5.

We have a decimal system using 10 digits: 0 1 2 3 4 5 6 7 8 and 9.

The 5 in 35 is worth 5 units but the 5 in 53 is 10 times bigger and is worth 5 tens or fifty.

We have the following columns:

Thousands	Hundreds	Tens	Units

Each column is ten times bigger than the one to the right.

Thousands	Hundreds	Tens	Units
4	0	7	3

In the above number, we have 4 thousands, 0 hundreds, 7 tens and 3 units ie 4073

The system continues with decimal numbers, where we use numbers less than 1 but more than 0.

Units	tenths	hundredths	thousandths

Still each column is ten times bigger than the one to the right.

Units	tenths	hundredths	thousandths
2	3	0	7

In the above number, we have 2 units, 3 tenths, 0 hundredths and 7 thousandths ie 2.307

We can only add and subtract tenths to tenths or hundredths to hundredths.

5.43	5.43	5.43	6.4
3	2.5	2.5	3
is right	is right	is wrong	is wrong

Both sets of columns can be combined to form the columns below:

N.B. The decimal point <u>always</u> goes between the <u>Units</u> and the <u>tenths</u>.

Thousands	Hundreds	Tens	Units	tenths	hundredths	thousandths

Multiplying

× by 10

Move numbers <u>one</u> place to the left
or decimal point appears to move <u>one</u> place to the right

eg 3.215 × 10 = 32.15
    46   × 10 = 460

× by 100

Move numbers <u>two</u> places to the left
or decimal point appears to move <u>two</u> places to the right

eg 2.618 × 100 = 261.8
    46   × 100 = 4600

× by 1000

Move numbers <u>three</u> places to the left
or decimal point appears to move <u>three</u> places to the right

eg 2.37   × 1000 = 2370
    46   × 1000 = 46000
    0.0324 × 1000 = 32.4

Dividing

÷ by 10

Move numbers <u>one</u> place to the right
or decimal point appears to move <u>one</u> place to the left

eg 2.568 ÷ 10 = 0.2568
    46   ÷ 10 = 4.6
    0.6   ÷ 10 = 0.06

÷ by 100

Move numbers <u>two</u> places to the right
or decimal point appears to move <u>two</u> places to the left

eg 5.123 ÷ 100 = 0.05123
    4666   ÷ 100 = 46.66

÷ by 1000

Move numbers <u>three</u> places to the right
or decimal point appears to move <u>three</u> places to the left

eg 2.37   ÷ 1000 = 0.00237
    4650   ÷ 1000 = 4.65

Adding and Subtracting Decimals 9

Remember that: 8 can be written as 8.0 or 8.00 or 8.000 etc.

23.4 can be written as 23.40 or 23.400 or 23.4000 etc.

Adding

Make sure that you know where the decimal point is in each number to be added.

Line up the decimal points

Fit numbers carefully into columns

The number you are subtracting always goes at the bottom

Always fill in 0's if there are blank spaces

Example A

Work out 3.41 + 2.8 + 9

```
  3.41
  2.80
  9.00  +
 15.21
```

Subtracting

Line up the decimal points

Fit numbers carefully into columns

Example B

Work out 6 - 2.34

```
       9
    5 10 10
    6.0 0
    2.3 4  -
    3.6 6
```

Decimals: division

Dividing by whole numbers

Lay out the division sum as normal.
Decimal points stay in line.

$$3 \underline{\smash{|4.47}} \atop 1.49$$

Add more noughts if needed.

$$5 \underline{\smash{|24.10}} \atop 4.82$$

Some may recur.

$$3 \underline{\smash{|0.490000}} \atop 0.163333$$ ans: $0.16\dot{3}$

Dividing by decimals

Step 1   Make right hand number into a whole number by multiplying by 10, 100, 1000 as necessary.

$1.625 \div 0.05$

multiply 0.05 by 100 to get 5

Step 2   Do the same to the left hand number.

multiply 1.625 by 100 to get 162.5

Step 3   Do the division as above.

$$5 \underline{\smash{|162.5}} \atop 32.5$$ ans: 32.5

Do not confuse with multiplication where you put the decimal places back.

Examples of how to begin divisions

a) $3.45 \div 0.3 \;=\; 34.5 \div 3$ *(each number has been multiplied by 10)*

b) $72 \div 0.05 \;=\; 7200 \div 5$ *(each number has been multiplied by 100)*

c) $8.1 \div 0.09 \;=\; 810 \div 9$ *(each number has been multiplied by 100)*

d) $0.5678 \div 0.18 = 56.78 \div 18$ *(each number has been multiplied by 100)*

Decimals: multiplication

In multiplication of decimals, there are three steps to follow.

Step 1	Underline <u>decimal places</u>. (digits after the point)	32.<u>5</u> x 0.<u>9</u>

Step 2 Do the multiplication without the points and any left hand noughts.

$$
\begin{array}{r}
325 \\
9 \ \times \\
\hline
2925
\end{array}
$$

Step 3 Count the <u>total</u> number of decimal places in the question and make sure the answer has the same number of decimal places.

2 dps

so 32.<u>5</u> x 0.<u>9</u> = 29.<u>25</u>

In this process we are multiplying each number by 10, 100, 1000, etc... in order to get rid of the decimal points, working out the new product and then reversing the effect of the multiplication by dividing by 10, 100, 1000, etc...

Example

Step 1 0.<u>28</u> x 0.<u>2</u>

Before doing the multiplication, estimate the answer

Step 2
$$
\begin{array}{r}
28 \\
2 \ \times \\
\hline
56
\end{array}
$$

Step 3 3 dps

so 0.<u>28</u> x 0.<u>2</u> = 0.<u>056</u>

(here we have to put in an extra nought to make 3 decimal places)

MATHS NOTEBOOK

To the Nearest .....

Sometimes an exact answer isn't needed. An answer of 34 562m is silly if you are measuring a distance. We can <u>approximate</u>.

34 562	Look at:		Answer
to the nearest 10	Units:	2 low	34 560
to the nearest 100	10s:	6 high	34 600
to the nearest 1000	100s:	5 high	35 000
to the nearest 10000	1000s:	2 low	30 000

The digits 0, 1, 2, 3, 4 are low and don't affect the previous number.
The digits 5, 6, 7, 8, 9 are high and bump the previous number up by 1.

Use approximations:

a) to avoid silly measurements;

b) for quick checks (eg 29 + 83 + 42 ≈ 30 + 80 + 40 = 150)

With decimals we can approximate in the same way:

0.1362	Look at:		Answer
to the nearest tenth	hundredths:	3 low	0.1
to the nearest hundredth	thousandths:	6 high	0.14
to the nearest thousandth	ten thousandths:	2 low	0.136

Decimal Places

Decimal Places

The digits <u>after</u> a decimal point are called <u>decimal places</u>; noughts <u>are</u> included.

Examples   21.<u>53</u> has 2 decimal places (2 dps)

6.<u>807</u> has 3 dps

0.<u>0041</u> has 4 dps

120.<u>00</u> has 2 dps

Correcting using decimal places

When correcting a number to say 2 decimal places, always look at the third decimal place to see if it is low or high. For 4 dps, look at the fifth etc...

Examples

Decimal Places	0.0838	13.10488
4	0.0838	13.1049
3	0.084	13.105
2	0.08	13.10 **
1	0.1	13.1

** You must never approximate from a previous approximation, so this is not 13.11
   Always approximate from the original number.

Significant Figures

14

Significant figures

The first significant figure in a number is the first non-zero digit reading from the left. **All** the following digits are significant, except noughts in whole numbers.

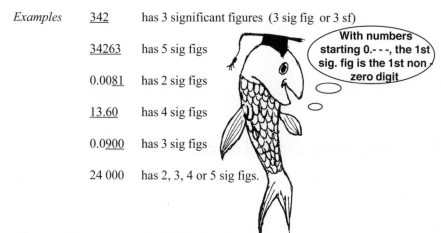

Examples		
342	has 3 significant figures (3 sig fig or 3 sf)	
34263	has 5 sig figs	
0.0081	has 2 sig figs	
13.60	has 4 sig figs	
0.0900	has 3 sig figs	
24 000	has 2, 3, 4 or 5 sig figs.	

With numbers starting 0.- - -, the 1st sig. fig is the 1st non zero digit

Correcting to n significant figures

When correcting to say 2 significant figures, always look at the third to see if it is low or high.

Sig Fig	2853.02899	3049	0.0025801
9	2853.02899		
8	2853.0290		
7	2853.029		
6	2853.03		
5	2853.0		0.0025801
4	2853	3049	0.002580
3	2850	3050	0.00258
2	2900	3000 **	0.0026
1	3000	3000	0.003

** You must never approximate from a previous approximation, so this is not 3100. Always approximate from the original number.

Approximating to 1 significant figure

An approximation to 1 significant figure is the roughest possible answer you can get and gives you a good idea of the size of the answer.

Example

Estimate $\dfrac{3.93 \times 4.38}{62.4}$ to 1 significant figure.

Step 1	Change all the numbers to 2 sig figs	$\dfrac{3.9 \times 4.4}{62}$
Step 2	Work out each part to 2 sig figs	$\dfrac{17}{62}$
Step 3	Give answer to 2 sig figs	$\dfrac{17}{62} = 0.27 \ (2 \text{ sf})$
Step 4	Round off answer to 1 sig fig	0.3

When estimating to 2 sig figs,
do all the working to 3 sig figs
and then round down at the final stage.

Make sure that your approximation is roughly correct

Common Errors

a) Saying that $3408 = 3$ to 1 sig fig
   instead of 3000

b) Saying that $0.349 = 0.4$ to 1 sig fig
   instead of 0.3
   (only the second sig fig can affect the first)

Measuring

Length

We use <u>millimetres</u> (<u>mm</u>), <u>centimetres</u> (<u>cm</u>), <u>decimetres</u> (<u>dm</u>), <u>metres</u> (<u>m</u>) and <u>kilometres</u> (<u>km</u>) to measure <u>length</u> or <u>distance</u>.

1 km = 1000 m   so   1 m = 0.001 km

1 m = 1000 mm   so   1 mm = 0.001 m

1 m = 100 cm   so   1 cm = 0.01 m

1 dm = 10 cm   so   1 cm = 0.1 dm

1 cm = 10 mm   so   1 mm = 0.1 cm

So 2.4 cm = 2 cm 4 mm

m km	⇨	km m	div by 1000 mult by 1000	mm m	⇨	m mm	div by 1000 mult by 1000
cm m	⇨	m cm	div by 100 mult by 100c	mm m	⇨	cm mm	div by 10 mult by 10

When writing small units as larger units, there are less of them so always DIVIDE.

When writing large units as smaller units, there are more of them so always MULTIPLY.

Mass

We use <u>grams</u> (<u>g</u>), <u>milligrams</u> (<u>mg</u>) and <u>tonnes</u> (<u>t</u>) to measure <u>mass</u>.

1000 mg = 1 g so   1 mg = 0.001 g

1000 g = 1 kg so   1 g = 0.001 kg

1000 kg = 1 t   so   1 kg = 0.001 t

g kg	⇨	kg g	div by 1000 mult by 1000	mg g	⇨	g mg	div by 1000 mult by 1000

Measuring

Capacity

We use <u>litres</u> (<u>l</u>) and <u>millilitres</u> (<u>ml</u>) to measure <u>capacity</u>.

1000 ml = 1 l   so   1 ml = 0.001 l

100 cl = 1 l   so   1 cl = 0.01 l

Note that 1 ml = 1 cc = 1 cm³ or 1 g of water.

| ml | | l | div by 1000 | cl | | l | div by 100 |
| l | | ml | mult by 1000 | l | | cl | mult by 100 |

Imperial Units

Here are some rough approximate equivalents with older non-metric imperial measurements:

1 inch (") = 2.54 cm   1 pound (lb) = 0.45 kg   1 pint = 0.57 l

1 foot (') = 30.5 cm   2.2 pounds = 1 kg   1 gallon = 4.55 l

1 yard = 91.5 cm

5 miles = 8 km

Time

12 hour clock	24 hour clock
a.m. (ante meridiem) is used for mornings (before noon). p.m. (post meridiem) is used for afternoons and evenings (after noon).	time is measured from 00:00 to 23:59 Noon is 12:00 (read as 12 hundred hours). For afternoon times add 12 hours to the 12 hour clock time e.g. 3.42 p.m. = 15:42
7.30 p.m.	19:30
5.23 a.m.	05:23
5.23 p.m.	17:23

Time intervals

Example A

How long is it from 6.30 p.m. to 7.20 p.m.?

Always work in convenient stages, for example by going up to a whole number of hours.

6.30 p.m. ⇨ 7.00 p.m. ⇨ 7.20 p.m.
     30 mins   +   20 mins   Ans: 50 mins

Example B

A train starts a journey at 07:18 and finishes at 11:10. How long is the journey?

07:18 ⇨ 07:30 ⇨ 08:00 ⇨ 11:00 ⇨ 11:10
   12 mins   +   30 mins   +   3 hours   +   10 mins
                                  Ans: 3hours 52 mins

Adding and subtracting times

<u>Never</u> use a decimal point. <u>Times are not decimals</u>. Beware of the Calculator!

Distance, Speed and Time

Examples

If a car travels 100 miles in 4 hours, its average speed is $100 \div 4 = 25$ mph.

This is <u>not</u> the actual speed, which may vary throughout the journey. The average speed is the speed which would have the same final effect if it had been constant.

If the car goes 200 km at 40 km/h, it will take $200 \div 40 = 5$ hours.

If it has an overall average speed of 35 km/h over 3 hours, it will travel $35 \times 3 = 105$ km.

<u>Rules</u>

Distance = **Speed x Time**

Speed **=** **<u>Distance</u>** (Think of miles <u>per</u> hour)
Time

Time **=** **<u>Distance</u>**
Speed

These <u>formulae</u> can be summarised by this triangle:

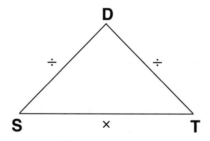

NB If a train travels at a constant speed of 100 km/h, then it will travel:

100 km in 1 hour
200 km in 2 hours
300 km in 3 hours

50 km in ½ hour
25 km in ¼ hour etc...

Equivalent Fractions

The diagram shows 3 equal pieces with one shaded.

ie $\frac{1}{3}$ is shaded

This diagram shows 6 equal pieces with two shaded.

ie $\frac{2}{6}$ is shaded

As both shaded parts are equal we say that $\frac{2}{6}$ is <u>equivalent</u> to $\frac{1}{3}$ ie $\frac{2}{6} = \frac{1}{3}$

This diagram shows that

$\frac{1}{3}$ and $\frac{3}{9}$ are equal or equivalent

To get equivalent fractions, we *multiply* or *divide* the top <u>and</u> the bottom of a fraction by the same number. Look at these examples:

$$\overset{\times 2}{\frac{1}{3}} = \frac{2}{6} \underset{\times 2}{}$$ $$\overset{\times 3}{\frac{1}{3}} = \frac{3}{9} \underset{\times 3}{}$$ $$\overset{\times 2}{\frac{2}{3}} = \frac{4}{6} \underset{\times 2}{}$$ $$\overset{\times 4}{\frac{3}{4}} = \frac{12}{16} \underset{\times 4}{}$$

$$\overset{\div 2}{\frac{6}{8}} = \frac{3}{4} \underset{\div 2}{}$$ $$\overset{\div 5}{\frac{10}{15}} = \frac{2}{3} \underset{\div 5}{}$$ When *dividing*, we call this <u>reducing</u> fractions to their <u>lowest terms</u>.

Note that *adding* or *subtracting* to the top and bottom *does not work*.

$$\overset{+ 1}{\frac{1}{2}} = \frac{2}{3} \underset{+ 1}{}$$

   **X**

Mixed Numbers & Improper Fractions

These are <u>mixed numbers</u>: $3\frac{1}{9}$ $1\frac{3}{5}$ $32\frac{2}{7}$ (a mixture of wholes and bits)

An <u>improper</u> fraction is a top-heavy one where the <u>numerator</u> (top) is larger than the <u>denominator</u> (bottom).

$$\frac{15}{8} \quad \frac{9}{5} \quad \frac{5}{4} \quad \frac{3}{1}$$

Changing a mixed number to an improper fraction

Sometimes you need to do this at the <u>start</u> of a fraction problem.

Example $2\frac{4}{5}$

Step 1   Whole number times denominator: $2 \times 5 = 10$

Step 2   Add numerator: $10 + 4 = 14$

Step 3   Put over denominator: $^{14}/_5$ or $\dfrac{14}{5}$

Changing a whole number to an improper fraction

Step 1   Just put it over 1   eg $3 = \dfrac{3}{1}$ **and** $25 = \dfrac{25}{1}$

Changing an improper fraction to a mixed number

Sometimes you need to do this at the <u>end</u> of a fraction problem.

Example $\dfrac{14}{3}$

Step 1   Divide numerator by denominator to get the whole number: $14 \div 3 = 4\,r\,2$

Step 2   Put remainder over the <u>denominator</u>. $4\frac{2}{3}$

If there is no remainder, just write the whole number. $\dfrac{9}{1} = 9$ $\dfrac{15}{3} = 5$

Adding Fractions

EXAMPLES (read each column downwards)	$\frac{3}{10} + \frac{3}{15}$	$\frac{5}{6} + \frac{2}{3}$	$2\frac{5}{6} + 1\frac{1}{2}$
Step 1 Add whole numbers			$3\frac{5}{6} + \frac{1}{2}$
Step 2 Find LCM of denominators			
Step 3 Put fractions over LCM using equivalent fractions	$\frac{9}{30} + \frac{6}{30}$	$\frac{5}{6} + \frac{4}{6}$	$3\frac{5}{6} + \frac{3}{6}$
Step 4 Add numerators Denominators stay the same	$\frac{15}{30}$	$\frac{9}{6}$	$3\frac{8}{6}$
Step 5 If result is improper, change to a mixed number		$1\frac{3}{6}$	$4\frac{2}{6}$
Step 6 Reduce fraction to its lowest terms, if necessary	$\frac{1}{2}$ (ans)	$1\frac{1}{2}$ (ans)	$4\frac{1}{3}$ (ans)

Only add fractions once their denominators are the same

Subtracting Fractions

EXAMPLES (read each column downwards)	$\frac{3}{10} - \frac{3}{15}$	$\frac{5}{6} - \frac{2}{3}$	$4\frac{2}{3} - 1\frac{1}{6}$	$5\frac{3}{8} - 2\frac{3}{4}$
Step 1 Subtract second whole number from first	↓	↓	$3\frac{2}{3} - \frac{1}{6}$	$3\frac{3}{8} - \frac{3}{4}$
Step 2 Find LCM of denominators **Step 3** Put fractions over LCM using equivalent fractions	$\frac{9}{30} - \frac{6}{30}$	$\frac{5}{6} - \frac{4}{6}$	$3\frac{4}{6} - \frac{1}{6}$	$3\frac{3}{8} - \frac{6}{8}$
Step 4 If second numerator is more than first, 'borrow' 1 whole and change it into smaller units	↓	↓	↓	$2\frac{8}{8}+\frac{3}{8}-\frac{6}{8}$
Step 5 Combine numerators. Denominators stay the same	$\frac{3}{30}$	$\frac{1}{6}$ (ans)	$3\frac{3}{6}$	$2\frac{5}{8}$ (ans)
Step 6 Reduce fraction to its lowest terms, if necessary	$\frac{1}{10}$ (ans)		$3\frac{1}{2}$ (ans)	

Only subtract fractions once their denominators are the same

Multiplying Fractions

EXAMPLES (read each column downwards)	$\frac{2}{3}$ x $\frac{1}{5}$	$\frac{5}{10}$ x $\frac{4}{7}$	$2\frac{1}{2}$ x $3\frac{1}{10}$	$\frac{3}{4}$ of $4\frac{2}{3}$
Step 1 Change to improper fractions "Of" mean "times"	↓	↓	$\frac{5}{2}$ x $\frac{31}{10}$	$\frac{3}{4}$ x $\frac{14}{3}$
Step 2 Cancel down any top number with any bottom number Repeat until no more cancelling possible	↓	$\frac{\cancel{5}^{1}}{\cancel{10}_{2}}$ x $\frac{\cancel{4}^{2}}{7}$	$\frac{\cancel{5}^{1}}{2}$ x $\frac{31}{\cancel{10}_{2}}$	$\frac{\cancel{3}^{1}}{\cancel{4}_{2}}$ x $\frac{\cancel{14}^{7}}{\cancel{3}_{1}}$
Step 3 Multiply top x top and bottom x bottom	$\frac{2 \times 1}{3 \times 5} = \frac{2}{15}$ (ans)	$\frac{1 \times 2}{1 \times 7} = \frac{2}{7}$ (ans)	$\frac{1 \times 31}{2 \times 2} = \frac{31}{4}$	$\frac{1 \times 7}{2 \times 1} = \frac{7}{2}$
Step 4 Change to mixed or whole number if improper			$7\frac{3}{4}$ (ans)	$3\frac{1}{2}$ (ans)

> Denominators do not have to be the same when multiplying fractions

Dividing Fractions

Division rule: Turn *right-hand* fraction upside down and then multiply.

Example

$$3\tfrac{3}{7} \text{ divided by } 2\tfrac{1}{10}$$

Step 1   Change to improper fractions: $\dfrac{24}{7} \quad \div \quad \dfrac{21}{10}$

Step 2   Turn *right-hand* fraction
upside down.

Change divide sign to multiply: $\dfrac{24}{7} \quad \times \quad \dfrac{10}{21}$

Step 3 etc   Continue as for multiplication.

Remember:

Turn Then Times

Fractions and Decimals

Changing decimals to fractions

Think of place value columns.

Step 1 If decimal has one decimal place (eg 0.<u>7</u>),   put over 10   ie $^7/_{10}$

If decimal has two decimal places (eg 0.<u>34</u>), put over 100   ie $^{34}/_{100}$

If decimal has three decimal places (eg 0.<u>613</u>), put over 1000 ie $^{613}/_{1000}$

Step 2 Reduce if necessary eg $0.\underline{75} = \frac{75}{100} = \frac{3}{4}$

NB Whole numbers stay the same   eg $3.\underline{4} = 3\frac{4}{10}$

Changing fractions to decimals

Step 1 Make the numerator look like a decimal $\frac{3}{4}$ becomes $\frac{3.0}{4}$

by writing .0 after it.

Step 2 Divide the numerator by the denominator,   ie $4\overline{)3.00}$

adding extra noughts if necessary. 0.75

NB Whole numbers stay the same   eg $3\frac{4}{5} = 3\frac{4.0}{5}$

$5\overline{)4.0}$
0.8

$3 + 0.8 = 3.8$ (ans)

Recurring decimals

Some fractions become <u>recurring</u> decimals. These are repeating decimals.

eg $\frac{8}{9} = 0.\dot{8}$ $\frac{83}{99} = 0.\dot{8}\dot{3}$ $\frac{1}{3} = 0.\dot{3}$ $\frac{5}{6} = 0.8\dot{3}$ $\frac{123}{999} = 0.\dot{1}2\dot{3}$

Ordering Fractions and Decimals 27

Example

Starting with the largest, put these in order of size: $\dfrac{3}{4}$, $\dfrac{5}{6}$, $\dfrac{18}{25}$, $\dfrac{31}{40}$

Step 1   Change fractions to decimals:

$$^3/_4 = 0.75$$
$$^5/_6 = 0.83333333....$$
$$^{18}/_{25} = 0.72$$
$$^{31}/_{40} = 0.775$$

Step 2   Look at units column: All 0 so look at next column.

Step 3   Look at tenths column
and place in order, largest
first:

$$^5/_6 = 0.83333333....$$
$$^3/_4 = 0.75$$
$$^{18}/_{25} = 0.72$$
$$^{31}/_{40} = 0.775$$

Step 4   Now look at hundredths column
of those with same tenths
digit, and put in order:

$$^5/_6 = 0.83333333....$$
$$^{31}/_{40} = 0.775$$
$$^3/_4 = 0.75$$
$$^{18}/_{25} = 0.72$$

So the order is $0.8\dot{3}$, 0.775, 0.75, 0.72 ie $^5/_6$ $^{31}/_{40}$ $^3/_4$ $^{18}/_{25}$

> **Decimals
> are easier to compare than
> fractions**

Percentages

Finding x% of a number

To work out x% of a number we work out $\dfrac{x}{100} \times \dfrac{number}{1}$

Examples

32% of 60 $= \dfrac{32}{100} \times \dfrac{60}{1} = \dfrac{32}{5} \times \dfrac{3}{1} = \dfrac{96}{5} = 19.2$

56% of 7.25   by calculator, work out: $56 \div 100 \times 7.25 = 4.06$

Writing one number as a percentage of another

Example

Express 4 as a percentage of 5

Step 1   Write as a fraction: $\dfrac{4}{5}$

Step 2   Multiply by 100: $\dfrac{4}{5} \times \dfrac{100}{1} = 80$

Step 3   Write % sign: 80% (ans)

Percentage Increase / Decrease / Profit / Loss

Use the formula: $\text{Percentage XXXXXXX} = \dfrac{\text{Actual XXXXXXX}}{\text{Starting Figure}} \times 100$

where XXXXXXX stands for increase, decrease, profit, loss etc...

<u>Ratios</u> are similar to fractions in that they can be reduced   eg 5:10 = 1:2

Sharing things using ratios

Always try to work out what **1** share is worth.

Example A

Split £36 in the ratio 4:5

We have a total of 4+5 = 9 shares = £36

$$\text{so } \mathbf{1} \text{ share} \quad = 36 \div 9 = \mathbf{£4}$$

so 4 shares   = 4 x **£4** = £16 ⎫   Check by adding
and 5 shares = 5 x **£4** = £20 ⎬   ie £16 + £20 = £36

Answer: £16 and £20

Example B

A sum of money is shared between Amy and Ben in the ratio 2:3. If Ben gets £15, how much does Amy get?

Ben gets 3 shares   = £15

so **1** share   = 15 ÷ 3 = **£5**

so Amy gets 2 shares   = 2 x **£5** = £10

Answer: Amy gets £10

Fractions / Percentages

34% means $\dfrac{34}{100}$ = $\dfrac{17}{50}$ ie 34 out of every 100

$\dfrac{3}{4}$ = $\dfrac{3}{4}$ x $\dfrac{100}{1}$ % = 75%

Decimals / Percentages

34%   = 0.34

0.27   = (0.27 x 100) %   = 27%
0.273   = (0.273 x 100) % = 27.3%
1.43   = (1.43 x 100) %   = 143%

Ratios / Fractions

1:3 = $\dfrac{1}{3}$

3:4 = $\dfrac{3}{4}$

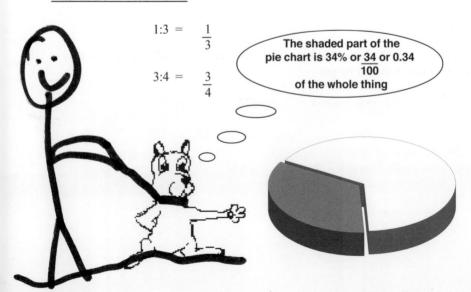

The shaded part of the
pie chart is 34% or $\dfrac{34}{100}$ or 0.34
of the whole thing

Positives and Negatives

Signs

The <u>sign</u> of a number shows us whether it is more than 0 (<u>positive</u> or +) or less than 0 (<u>negative</u> or -).

The sign always goes <u>before</u> the number eg +3, -4, -0.5, +2½ but not 4-, 3+.

If a number has <u>no sign</u>, then it is <u>positive</u>   eg 4 is really +4, and 3.5 is really +3.5

Negative numbers are often used to measure temperatures below zero and heights below sea level.

Adding and Subtracting

It is easiest to add and subtract numbers by moving along a number line.

So to <u>add</u> three we move 3 to the <u>right</u>.
　to <u>subtract</u> four we move 4 to the <u>left</u>.

So $2 + 3 = 5$
　　$2 - 3 = -1$
　　$-2 + 3 = 1$
　　$-2 - 3 = -5$

For more complicated calculations eg -3 + 4 - 2 + 6 we can combine the negatives to get -5 and then combine the positives to get +10 and then -5 + 10 = 5 (Ans).

Multiplying and Dividing

To multiply <u>positive</u> and <u>negative</u> numbers we look at a multiplication square which is really formed by repeated addition and subtraction (look for patterns).

x	3	2	1	0	-1	-2	-3
3	9	6	3	0	-3	-6	-9
2	6	4	2	0	-2	-4	-6
1	3	2	1	0	-1	-2	-3
0	0	0	0	0	0	0	0
-1	-3	-2	-1	0	1	2	3
-2	-6	-4	-2	0	2	4	6
-3	-9	-6	-3	0	3	6	9

Notice that when we multiply **two positves** or **two negatives** we get a positive

and when we multiply two numbers with different signs we get a negative.

To summarize, *when multiplying*:

With two signs the same you get a   + answer

With two different signs you get a   - answer

The same rules apply to *division*.

Examples

$14 \div -2 = -7$ (Different signs give you   - answers)
$-14 \div -2 = 7$ (Same signs give you   + answers)

Combinations of Signs

Change - - to +   Change - + to a -   Change + - to a -

Examples

$3 - -4 = 3 + 4 = 7$ $3 - +4 = 3 - 4 = -1$ $3 + -4 = 3 - 4 = -1$

Factor Trees

Example   **Write 36 as the product of its prime factors**

```
    36          or       36         or       36
   / \                  / \                  / \
  18   2               9   4                6   6
 / \   \              / \ / \              / \ / \
9   2   2            3  3 2  2            2  3 2  3
/ \   \   \
3  3   2   2
```

Thus **36 = 3 x 3 x 2 x 2**   (order does not matter and 2 and 3 are primes)

Division method

This will work as long as you always divide by a <u>prime</u> number, stopping when you get to 1.

```
2 | 36              3 | 36
2 | 18              3 | 12
3 | 9     or        2 | 4
3 | 3               2 | 2
    1                   1
```

So **36 = 2 x 2 x 3 x 3 or 2^2 x 3^2** using <u>indices</u>.

Square Roots

Example   **To find the square root of 784:**

Step 1   *Express 784 as the product of prime factors, using one of the above methods*

$$784 = 2^4 \times 7^2$$

Step 2   *Halve the indices (divide by 3 for the cube root)*

square root of $784 = 2^2 \times 7^1$

Step 3   *Work out value*

square root of $784 = 2 \times 2 \times 7 = 4 \times 7 = 28$

Step 4   Using symbols

$$\sqrt{784} = 28$$

Calculator Work

Apart from the number keys and basic +, - x, ÷ keys, there are several other important keys with which you should become familiar.

| +/- | Changes a + number to a - number and vice versa |

| Min | Clears the memory and puts whatever is on the screen into the memory |

| M+ | Adds whatever is on the screen to whatever is in the memory |

| M- | Subtracts whatever is on the screen from whatever is in the memory |

| MR or RM | Displays whatever is in the memory on the screen |

| (| Brackets: use as normal brackets |

| √ | <u>Square roots</u> whatever is on the screen |

Example A

Work out: $\dfrac{17.6 + 41.4}{37.97}$

Method 1 17.6 $\boxed{+}$ 41.4 $\boxed{=}$ $\boxed{÷}$ 37.97 $\boxed{=}$

Method 2 $\boxed{(}$ 17.6 $\boxed{+}$ 41.4 $\boxed{)}$ $\boxed{÷}$ 37.97 $\boxed{=}$

Example B

Work out: $\dfrac{17.6}{47.97 - 41.4}$

> Work out the denominator (bottom) first and store it in the memory

Method 1 17.6 $\boxed{÷}$ $\boxed{(}$ 47.97 $\boxed{-}$ 41.4 $\boxed{)}$ $\boxed{=}$

Method 2 47.97 $\boxed{-}$ 41.4 $\boxed{=}$ $\boxed{Min}$

17.6 $\boxed{÷}$ $\boxed{MR}$ $\boxed{=}$

Estimation

It is important to have a rough idea of the answer, before you use your calculator.
It is easy to make a mistake when using a calculator. For example, in Example A on
the previous page, a common mistake is to forget the = sign midway. This would
lead to you calculating 17.6 + 41.4 ÷ 37.97, which will give the wrong
answer as division takes priority over addition. So a good estimate would be
carried out as follows:

Write each number in the question to 1 sig. fig:

$$\frac{17.6 + 41.4}{37.97} \implies \frac{20 + 40}{40}$$

Then calculate, in your head, $20 + 40 = 60$ and then $60 ÷ 40 = 1.5$

VPAM

Many scientific calculators use VPAM logic. This means that calculations should be
entered in the same way that they are written.

Example A

Work out: $\sqrt{(24.3 + 7.6)}$

Method | √ | | (| 24.3 | + | 7.6 |) | = |

Example B

Work out: $24.3 + 7.6^2$

Method 1 24.3 | + | 7.6 | x^2 | = |

Method 2 24.3 | + | 7.6 | ^ | 2 | = |

> To square numbers use the power button or the x^2 button

Simple Algebra

Simplifying like terms

Only add like terms

a + a	= 2a
a + a + a	= 3a
2a + a	= 3a
5a + 4a	= 9a
2a + a + 3a	= 6a
2a + b + 3b	= 2a + 4b
3a + b - 2a + 4b	= a + 5b

Solving simple equations

Treat an equation as a balance and always do the same to both sides.

Example A

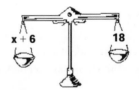

Solve	**x + 6**	**=**	**18**
Take 6 off both sides:	x + 6 - 6	=	18 - 6
Simplify:	x	=	12

Example B

Solve	**x - 4**	**=**	**8**
Add 4 to both sides:	x - 4 + 4	=	8 + 4
Simplify:	x	=	12

| *Example C* | | **3x** | **=** | **21** |

Divide both sides by 3:
$$\frac{3x}{3} = \frac{21}{3}$$

Simplify: $\qquad x = 7$

Example D

Solve $\qquad$ **3x** **=** **22**

> Answers should always read x=
>
> Always do the same to both sides

Divide both sides by 3:
$$\frac{3x}{3} = \frac{22}{3}$$

Simplify: $\qquad x = 7\frac{1}{3}$

Example E

Solve $\qquad$ **5x + 3** **=** **18**

Take 3 off both sides: $\qquad 5x + 3 - 3 = 18 - 3$

Simplify: $\qquad 5x = 15$

Divide both sides by 5:
$$\frac{5x}{5} = \frac{15}{5}$$

Simplify: $\qquad x = 3$

<u>Checking Answers</u>

Check answers by <u>substituting</u> your answer back into the original equation.

Example E (check)

If **x = 3**, then $5x + 3 = 5 \times 3 + 3 = 15 + 3 = 18$ which is correct.

Equations

Example F

Solve		**4x + 3**	**= 2x + 9**
Subtract 3 from both sides:		4x + 3 - 3 =	2x + 9 - 3
Simplify:		4x =	2x + 6
Subtract 2x from both sides:		4x - 2x =	2x + 6 - 2x
Simplify:		2x =	6
Divide both sides by 2:		$\frac{2x}{2}$ =	$\frac{6}{2}$
Simplify:		x =	3

Example G

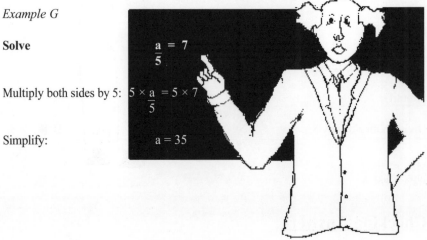

Solve $\frac{a}{5} = 7$

Multiply both sides by 5: $5 \times \frac{a}{5} = 5 \times 7$

Simplify: $a = 35$

Example H

Solve $\dfrac{3y}{4} + y = 7$

Multiply both sides by 4
and cancel 4s like fractions: $\cancel{4} \times \dfrac{3y}{\cancel{4}} + 4 \times y = 4 \times 7$

Simplify: $3y + 4y = 28$

Simplify: $7y = 28$

Divide both sides by 7: $\dfrac{7y}{7} = \dfrac{28}{7}$

Simplify: $y = 4$

> To get rid of fractions,
> multiply through by the
> bottom number

Example I

Solve $\dfrac{3y}{4} + \dfrac{y}{7} = 5$

Multiply both sides by 4
and cancel 4s: $\cancel{4} \times \dfrac{3y}{\cancel{4}} + 4 \times \dfrac{y}{7} = 4 \times 5$

Simplify: $3y + \dfrac{4y}{7} = 20$

Multiply both sides by 7
and cancel 7s: $7 \times 3y + \cancel{7} \times \dfrac{4y}{\cancel{7}} = 7 \times 20$

Simplify: $21y + 4y = 140$

                           $25y = 140$

Divide both sides by 25: $\dfrac{25y}{25} = \dfrac{140}{25}$

Simplify: $y = 5.6$

40 *Substituting and Simple Factorising*

Substitution

If $a = 3$, $b = 2$ and $c = 4$

then $2a \qquad = 2 \times 3 \qquad = 6$

$\quad a + b \qquad = 3 + 2 \qquad = 5$

$\quad a - c \qquad = 3 - 4 \qquad = -1$

$\quad a^2 \qquad = a \times a \qquad = 3 \times 3 \qquad = 9$

$\quad 2c^2 \qquad = 2 \times c \times c = 2 \times 4 \times 4 = 32$

$\quad (2c)^2 \qquad = 2c \times 2c = 8 \times 8 \qquad = 64$

Always multiply out brackets first

Brackets

$\quad 5(x + 2) \quad = 5x + 10$

$\quad 5(2x - 3) = 10x - 15$

$\quad -5(2x - 3) = -10x + 15$

$\quad 6(x + 2) - 3(x - 2) \quad = 6x + 12 - 3x + 6$

$\qquad\qquad\qquad\qquad\qquad = 3x + 18$

$\quad 3(2x + 3y - z) = 6x + 9y - 3z$

Simple Indices

An <u>index</u> is the power to which you raise a number. The index of x^{31} is 31.

$\quad a \times a \qquad = a^2$

$\quad a \times a \times a \quad = a^3$

$\quad a^2 \times a^3 \qquad = a^5$

Simple Factorising

Example	**Factorise $15x^2y^2 + 10xy^3$**	
Step 1	Find the highest number that goes into 15 and 10	5
Step 2	Write down the highest powers of x and y which can divide into x^2y^2 and xy^3	xy^2
Step 3	Divide both terms by 5 and by xy^2	$3x + 2y$
Step 4	The answer is:	$5xy^2(3x + 2y)$

<u>Adding & Subtracting</u>

We can only add or subtract like terms so:

$3a + a + 6b$ $=$ $4a + 6b$

$3xy + 6x - 7y + 7x$ $=$ $3xy + 13x - 7y$ (only the x's are similar)

$5x^2 - 2x$ does not simplify since x^2 and x are not similar

$5x^2y - 3x^2y$ $=$ $2x^2y$

<u>Multiplying</u>

We can multiply any terms together by:

     a) multiplying the numbers together
     b) adding the indices of like letters

When no index follows a term, it is the equivalent of it having an index of 1

So: $3a \times 4a$ $=$ $12a^2$

      $4ab \times 2a^2$ $=$ $8a^3b$

      $3a^2b^3 \times 4ab^2$ $=$ $12a^3b^5$

<u>Dividing</u>

We can divide any terms together by:

a) dividing the numbers by each other
b) subtracting the indices of like letters

So: $6a^3 \div 2a^2$ $=$ $3a$

      $8a^3b \div 4a$ $=$ $2a^2b$

      $12a^5b^3 \div 3a^2b$ $=$ $4a^3b^2$

      $7a^2b^3 \div 14a^3b^2$ $=$ $\dfrac{b}{2a}$

AHHH!

42 *Inequalities and Forming Equations*

Inequalities

Treat in the same way as equations, with one possible exception at the final stage:

If you change all the signs in an inequality make sure you turn the inequality sign over

If you reach, for example:	$-2x$	$<$	4
Change all the signs to:	$2x$	$>$	-4
	x	$>$	-2

If you reach:	$-3a$	$>$	-27

Change to:	$3a$	$<$	27
	a	$<$	9

Forming Equations

Example

Pencils cost x pence each, rulers cost twice as much and rubbers cost 5p more than pencils.
If I buy 3 pencils, a ruler and 2 rubbers, I spend 94p. How much does each item cost?

Write, in terms of x, the cost of each item:

Pencil	x pence
Ruler	2x pence
Rubber	x+5 pence

Write, in terms of x, the total cost: Cost = $3(x) + 2x + 2(x+5)$

Form an equation by putting this
<u>expression</u> equal to 94: $3(x) + 2x + 2(x+5) = 94$

Simplify and solve:

$$\mathbf{3x + 2x + 2x + 10 = 94}$$
$$7x + 10 = 94$$
$$7x = 84$$
$$x = 12$$

Write out cost of each item
(ie answer the question):

Pencil	x	= 12 pence
Ruler	2x	= 24 pence
Rubber	x+5	= 17 pence

MATHS NOTEBOOK

There are several methods for solving equations simultaneously (at the same time):
Substitution, Elimination, Graphically, Using Matrices.

Substitution

Example	**Solve simultaneously**	**3a + 2b = 7**
		4a + b = 6

Step 1	Label equations A and B	A) 3a + 2b = 7
		B) 4a + b = 6

Step 2   Choose equation with a single letter   B) 4a + b = 6
and rearrange it to make it the subject
Use brackets on the right hand side   B) b = (6-4a)

Step 3   Substitute this in place of this letter
in the other equation   A) 3a + 2(6-4a)=7

Step 4   Solve this equation   A) 3a + 12 - 8a = 7
                                        -5a + 12 = 7
                                        -5a = -5
                                        5a = 5
                                        a = 1

Step 5   Use this value to work out the
'single letter' from *Step 2*   B) b = 6 - 4a
                                      b = 6 - 4 × **1**
                                      b = 6 - 4 = 2

Step 6   Write out the full solution   **a = 1**
                                            b = 2

Step 7   Check answers by substituting back into other equation
3a + 2b = 3 × 1 + 2 × 2 = 3 + 4 = 7

Remember
that you have not finished
until step 7

Simultaneous Equations

Elimination

Use elimination when there are no 'single letters'.

Example	**Solve simultaneously**	$5a + 3b = 1$
		$2a - 5b = 19$

Step 1   Label the equations A and B

A) $\quad 5a + 3b = 1$
B) $\quad 2a - 5b = 19$

Step 2   Multiply A) by coefficient of a in B)
Multiply B) by coefficient of a in A)

2 x A) $\quad 10a + 6b = 2$
5 x B) $\quad 10a - 25b = 95$

Step 3   Add or subtract the two equations.
In this case we subtract because
the two 10a's are the same.
Use brackets to be safe

$(10a+6b) - (10a-25b) = 2-95$

Step 4   Simplify to work out the value of
this letter

$10a + 6b - 10a + 25b = -93$
$6b + 25b = -93$
$31b = -93$
$\mathbf{b = -3}$

Step 5   Use this value to work out the other
letter. Choose the simpler equation
to work from

A) $\quad 5a + 3b = 1$
$5a + 3 \times \textbf{-3} = 1$
$5a + \text{-9} = 1$
$5a = 10$
$\mathbf{a = 2}$

Step 6   Write out the full solution

$\mathbf{a = 2}$
$\mathbf{b = -3}$

Step 7   Check answers by substituting back into other equation
B) $2a - 5b = 2 \times 2 - 5 \times \textbf{-3} = 4 - \text{-15} = 4 + 15 = 19$

Graphical Method

Example	**Solve simultaneously**	$5x + 3y = 1$
		$2x - 5y = 19$

Step 1   Label equations A and B

Step 2   Plot A and B on a set of coordinate axes

Step 3   Write down the coordinates of the point
where A and B intersect (cross)

$(2, -3)$

Step 4   Write out full solution

$\mathbf{x = 2}$
$\mathbf{y = -3}$

Trial and Improvement

Some <u>equations</u> can be solved by trying out a number and improving on the "guess". With the use of a calculator, fairly accurate solutions can be found.

Example A

Solve: $x(x + 1) = 4$

Value of x	Value of x(x + 1)	Too big / Too small
2	6	too big
1	2	too small
1.5	3.75	too small
1.7	4.59	too big
1.6	4.16	too big
1.55	3.9525	too small

This shows that 1<x<2

From this we can tell that the solution of $x(x + 1) = 4$ is x = 1.6 (2 sig fig)

Example B

Find: **The smallest positive integer x such that $x(x + 2) > 200$**

Value of x	Value of x(x + 2)	Too big / Too small
10	120	too small
15	255	too big
12	168	too small
14	224	too big
13	195	too small

From this we can tell that the answer is 14

Sequences

There are some important sequences which should be easily spotted.
It always helps to look at the gaps between numbers when looking for patterns.

Even Numbers	2, 4, 6, 8, 10...	$2n$
Odd Numbers	1, 3, 5, 7, 9...	$2n-1$
Square Numbers	1, 4, 9, 16, 25...	n^2
Cube Numbers	1, 8, 27, 64, 125...	n^3
Triangle Numbers	1, 3, 6, 10, 15...	$\frac{1}{2}n(n+1)$
Powers of 2	1, 2, 4, 8, 16, 32...	2^n
Multiples of 4	4, 8, 12, 16, 20...	$4n$
Gaps of 4	5, 9, 13, 17, 21...	$4n+1$
Gaps of 4	6, 10, 14, 18, 22...	$4n+2$
Fibonnaci	1, 1, 2, 3, 5, 8...	Add two terms to get next

<u>Notation</u>

We sometimes call the first term of a sequence T_1, the second T_2, the third T_3, etc...

The nth term is thus called T_n

Example **Write out the first four terms of the sequence given by $T_n = n^2 - 3$**

Putting n = **1** we get $T_1 = 1^2 - 3 = 1 - 3 \quad = -2$
Putting n = **2** we get $T_2 = 2^2 - 3 = 4 - 3 \quad = 1$
Putting n = **3** we get $T_3 = 3^2 - 3 = 9 - 3 \quad = 6$
Putting n = **4** we get $T_4 = 4^2 - 3 = 16 - 3 \quad = 13$

Thus the first four terms of the sequence are -2, 1, 6, 13

Coordinates and Straight Line Equations 47

Coordinates

Coordinates are used to give the address or position of a point.

We use two <u>axes</u>, the <u>x-axis</u> and the <u>y-axis</u>. The axes meet at the <u>origin</u> (0,0).

A point has two coordinates, the x coordinate and the y coordinate. The coordinates are always put in brackets and are separated by a comma: (x, y)

Examples

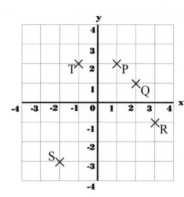

P	is at (1,2)
Q	is at (2,1)
R	is at (3,-1)
S	is at (-2,-3)
T	is at (-1,2)

Straight Line Equations

x = lines are <u>vertical</u>   y = lines are <u>horizontal</u>

The line x = 3 joins up all points whose x-coordinate is 3   eg (3, 4), (3, -1), (3, 0) ...

Note that

the <u>y-axis</u>
is x = 0

and

the <u>x-axis</u>
is y = 0

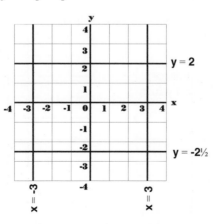

y = 2

y = -2½

48 *Sloping Lines and Gradients*

Gradient

The gradient of a line is a mathematical way of saying how steep it is.
Here are some examples:

gradient = 0   gradient = 1   gradient = -1   gradient = ∞

Lines which slope up from left to right have + gradients

Lines which slope down from left to right have - gradients

To Measure Gradients

Step 1   Build a step below the line, using
               horizontal and vertical lines

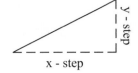

Step 2   Using any unit of measurement,
               measure the x - step and the y - step   eg: x - step = 4 cm
                                                                  y - step = 2 cm

Step 3   Work out $\dfrac{\text{y - step}}{\text{x - step}}$ **Gradient** = $\dfrac{\textbf{y - step}}{\textbf{x - step}} = \dfrac{2}{4} = \dfrac{1}{2}$

Sloping Line Equations

When the equation is in the form **y = mx + c**, m is the gradient
and c is the intercept on the y-axis.

Examples

Line	Equation	Gradient	Intercept on y-axis
A	y=3x+1	3	1
B	y=x-2	1	-2
C	y=4-2x	-2	4

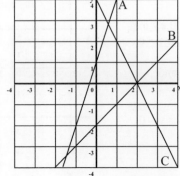

Plotting Curves

Use a table to work out y - values.
Note that straight lines can also be <u>plotted </u>in this way.

Example   Plot $y = x^2 + 3$

x - values	-3	-2	-1	0	1	2	3
y - values	12	7	4	3	4	7	12

The y - values are obtained by working out $x^2 + 3$ for each **x** - value.

Now plot the points (-3, 12), (-2, 7), (-1, 4) etc. and join them up with a <u>smooth</u> curve. Do *not* join them up with *straight* lines.

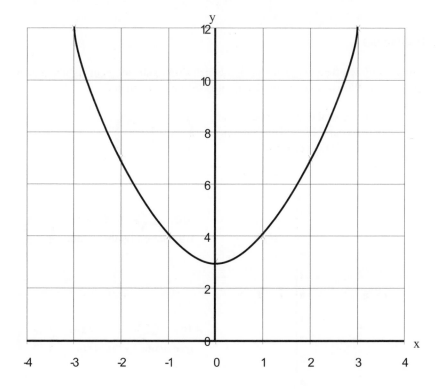

50 *Reflections and Translations*

Reflections

A <u>reflection</u> is a type of <u>transformation</u> which flips a shape across a <u>mirror line</u>. We use an equation to identify the mirror line.

Example

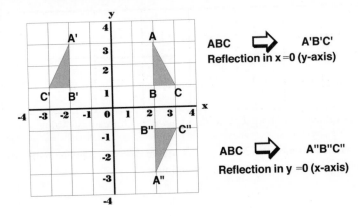

ABC ⟹ A'B'C'
Reflection in x = 0 (y-axis)

ABC ⟹ A"B"C"
Reflection in y = 0 (x-axis)

Translations

A <u>translation</u> is a type of <u>transformation</u> which shifts a shape <u>left or right</u> and then <u>up or down</u>. We use a vector to identify this shifting movement.

In a vector the top number is the horizontal shift, and the bottom number is the vertical shift.

$$\begin{pmatrix} \xleftarrow{-} \; \xrightarrow{+} \\ \updownarrow \begin{smallmatrix} + \\ - \end{smallmatrix} \end{pmatrix}$$

Example

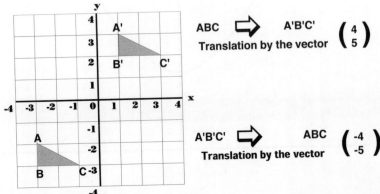

ABC ⟹ A'B'C'
Translation by the vector $\begin{pmatrix} 4 \\ 5 \end{pmatrix}$

A'B'C' ⟹ ABC
Translation by the vector $\begin{pmatrix} -4 \\ -5 \end{pmatrix}$

Rotations

A <u>rotation</u> is a type of <u>transformation</u> which turns a shape around a fixed point. We use *three* pieces of information to identify a rotation:

1)   the <u>angle</u> of the turn

2)   the <u>centre</u> of the turn (ie the fixed point)

3)   the <u>direction</u> (ie <u>clockwise</u> or <u>anticlockwise</u>)

Remember:
if the direction is not
given, take it to be
anticlockwise.

Example

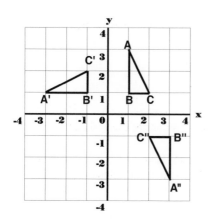

ABC ⇨ A'B'C'
Rotation through 90° anticlockwise about (0,0)

ABC ⇨ A"B"C"
Rotation through 180 (anticlockwise) about (2,0)

Enlargements

When we <u>enlarge</u> an object its size changes but its shape remains the same.

We need to give two pieces of information:

1)   the <u>centre</u> of the enlargement

2)   the <u>scale factor</u>

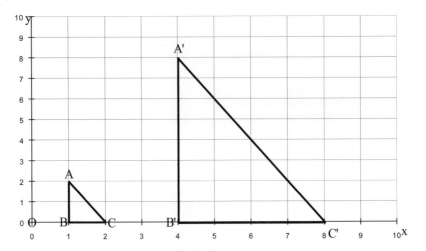

Trangle ABC has been enlarged by scale factor 4, centre O.

Notice that: OB = 1 unit and OB'   = 4 units
                            AB = 2 units and A'B' = 8 units

Also notice that the area of $\triangle A'B'C'$ is 4^2 i.e. 16 times bigger than the area of $\triangle ABC$.

<u>Congruence and Similarity</u>

Two figures which are identical in shape and size are <u>congruent</u>. All angles and all lengths must match. They may be rotations or reflections of each other.

Two figures which are identical in shape are <u>similar</u>. Their angles will match and their lengths will be in proportion. They may be rotations or reflections of each other but will also be enlarged.

Symmetry

Line (Reflection) Symmetry

An <u>axis of symmetry</u> or <u>mirror line</u> splits a shape into two matching parts.

The axis of symmetry is sometimes shown by a dotted line.

These shapes have 3 lines of symmetry:

These shapes have 2 lines of symmetry:

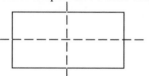

These shapes have no lines of symmetry:

Rotational Symmetry

If we rotate a shape <u>one complete turn</u>, it may look the same at certain stages. The number of times it looks the same is called the <u>order of rotational symmetry</u>.
All shapes have at least order 1.

Examples

Order 4   **Order 2**   **Order 3**   **Order 5**   **Order ∞**

Polygons

A <u>polygon</u> is a many-sided or many-angled shape.
Greek: polu means many; gõnia means angles.

Type of Polygon	Number of Sides	Special types
<u>Triangle</u>	3	<u>Scalene</u>, <u>isosceles</u>, <u>equilateral</u>, <u>right-angled</u>.
<u>Quadrilateral</u>	4	<u>Square</u>, <u>rectangle</u>, <u>rhombus</u>, <u>parallelogram</u>, <u>kite</u>, <u>trapezium</u>, <u>isosceles trapezium</u>, <u>arrowhead</u>.
<u>Pentagon</u>	5	<u>regular</u>, <u>irregular</u>
<u>Hexagon</u>	6	regular, irregular
<u>Heptagon</u>	7	regular, irregular
<u>Octagon</u>	8	regular, irregular
<u>Nonagon</u>	9	regular, irregular
<u>Decagon</u>	10	regular, irregular

Quadrilateral	Diagram	Angles	Sides	Lines of Symmetry	Rotational Symmetry
Square		all equal to 90°	all equal, opposites parallel	4	order 4
Rectangle		all equal to 90°	opposites equal and parallel	2	order 2
Rhombus		opposites equal	opposites equal and parallel	2	order 2
Parallelogram		opposites equal	opposites equal and parallel	0	order 2
Kite		one pair of opposites equal	2 adjacent equal pairs	1	no rotational symmetry (order 1)
Trapezium		nothing special	one pair parallel	0	no rotational symmetry
Isosceles Trapezium		2 adjacent pairs equal	one pair equal	1	no rotational symmetry

Solids

Prisms

Prisms have the same cross-section all the way through, like a telephone message block.

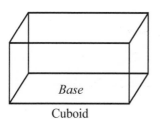
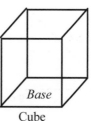
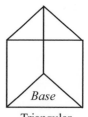

Cylinder   Cuboid   Cube   Triangular Based Prism

Pyramids

Pyramids have a flat base and rise to a point.

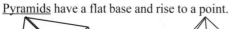
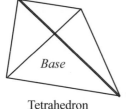

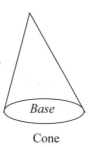
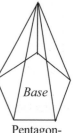

Tetrahedron   Square-Based Pyramid   Cone   Pentagon-Based Pyramid

Spheres

Spheres are like footballs, squash balls, netballs etc...

Sphere

Do not confuse spheres with circles. Circles are 2D shapes which are not solid objects.

MATHS NOTEBOOK

The <u>perimeter</u> of a shape is the distance all the way around its edge.

Start at one corner and <u>add</u> up all the lengths of each side as you go once around the edge.

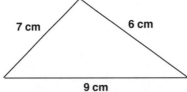

For this <u>triangle</u>, the perimeter = 6 + 7 + 9 = 22cm

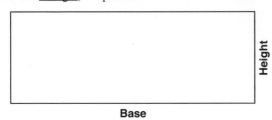

For a <u>rectangle</u> the perimeter is double (the base + the height)

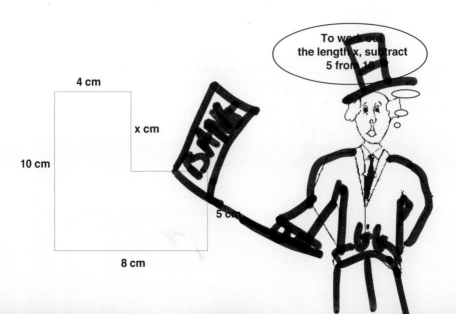

Area

<u>Area</u> is a measure of space inside a closed 2D shape.
This is a centimetre square. We write its area as <u>1 cm^2</u> or 1 square centimetre or 1 sq. cm.

We use this square to measure the area of larger shapes.

Rectangles

This <u>rectangle </u>has an area of 15 cm^2 because 15 centimetre squares fit inside it.

A quicker way to work out the area of a rectangle is to multiply the length of its base by its height.   In this case Area = 5 × 3 = 15 cm^2.

Learn this formula: **<u>Area of rectangle = Base × Height</u>**

This is sometimes written as   Area of rectangle = length × breadth, but this is exactly the same.

Triangles
Learn this formula:
<u>Area of triangle = Base × Height ÷ 2</u> or <u>Area of triangle = 1/2 Base × Height</u>

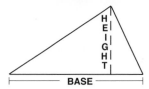 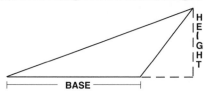

Parallelograms

Learn this formula: <u>**Area of parallelogram = Base × Height**</u>

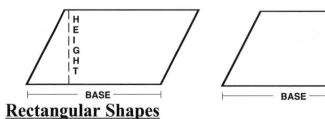

Rectangular Shapes

Split into rectangular pieces and then add or subtract the areas:

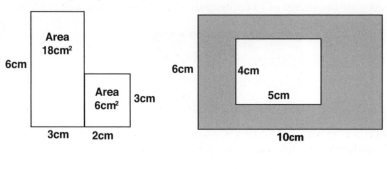

Area = 18 + 6
  = 24 cm²

Area = (6 × 10) - (4 × 5)
  = 60   -   20
  = 40 cm²

Trapezia

Learn this formula: <u>**Area of trapezium = Average of parallel sides x height**</u>

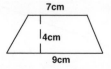

Area = $\frac{1}{2}(7 + 9) \times 4$
  = 8 × 4
  = 32 cm²

Volume is a measure of the amount of space contained in a 3D solid object.

This is a diagram of a centimetre cube. We write its volume as 1 cm³ or 1 cubic centimetre or 1 cu. cm or 1 cc (for fluids).

We use this cube to measure the volume of larger shapes such as cuboids.

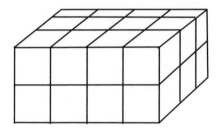

This cuboid has a volume of 24 cm³ because 24 centimetre cubes fit inside it.

Learn this formula: **Volume of Cuboid = Length x Width x Height**

Surface area is a measure of the total area of *all* the faces of a solid.

Looking at the net of a solid helps to work out its surface area:

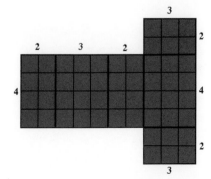

$$4 \times 2 = 8$$
$$4 \times 2 = 8$$
$$4 \times 3 = 12$$
$$4 \times 3 = 12$$
$$2 \times 3 = 6$$
$$2 \times 3 = \underline{\ 6}$$
Surface Area $= 52$ cm²

Types of Angle

Angles are measured in <u>degrees</u> with a <u>protractor</u>.

Angles are made up of two arms opening out at a point.

Types of Angle

Acute Angles   Between 0° and 90°

Right Angles   Exactly 90°

Obtuse Angles   Between 90° and 180°

Straight Line Angles   Exactly 180°

Reflex Angles   Between 180° and 360°

Basic Angle Rules

There are 360° at a point.

So angles at a point always add up to 360°.

There are 180° on a straight line so angles on a straight line always add up to 180°.

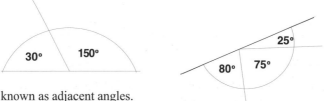

These are known as <u>adjacent</u> angles.

<u>Parallel</u> lines are ones which never meet. They point in the same direction and are always the same distance apart. Pairs of similar arrows are used to show that lines are parallel.

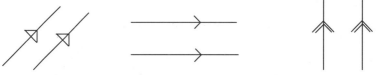

<u>Perpendicular</u> lines are ones which meet at 90° or at <u>right angles</u>. Square boxes are used to show that lines are perpendicular.

<u>Horizontal</u> lines are ones which are flat and parallel to the horizon.

<u>Vertical</u> lines are ones which are upright and perpendicular to the horizon.

Triangles

The <u>interior</u> (inside) angles of a <u>triangle</u> always add up to 180°.

 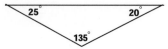

NB: The interior angles of a <u>quadrilateral</u> always add up to 360°.

 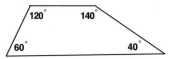

<u>Types of Triangle</u>

<u>Isosceles</u> triangles have two equal sides and two equal angles.
Pairs of equal angles are marked. Pairs of equal sides are also marked.

<u>Equilateral</u> triangles have all three angles equal and all three sides equal.
The sides can be any length (and equal), but the angles are always 60°.

 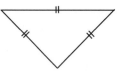

<u>Right-angled</u> triangles have a 90° or right angle in them.

 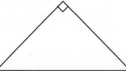

<u>Scalene</u> triangles have all three angles different and all three sides of different
lengths.

 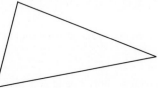

Angles and Parallel Lines

MATHS NOTEBOOK

Vertically Opposite

Vertically opposite angles are found when two straight lines cross over. They are opposite each other, form X shapes and are <u>equal</u>.

Adjacent

Adjacent angles are found on a straight line.
They are next to each other and <u>add up to 180°</u>.

Alternate

Alternate angles are found when a line lies across <u>parallel</u> lines.
Alternate angles form Z or S shapes and are <u>equal.</u>

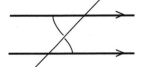

Corresponding

Corresponding angles are also found when a line lies across <u>parallel</u> lines.
Corresponding angles form F shapes and are <u>equal</u>.

Interior (Allied)

Interior or allied angles are also found when a line lies across <u>parallel</u> lines.
Interior or allied angles form C shapes and <u>add up to 180°</u>.

What's the difference?

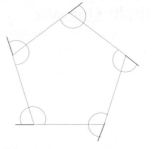

In this <u>polygon</u> the <u>exterior</u> angles are the ones that are outside the shape, and the <u>interior</u> angles are the ones inside the shape.

Exterior Angles always add up to 360°

In any closed convex polygon, regular or irregular, the sum of the exterior angles is always 360°.

In a regular polygon this is useful, because all the exterior angles are equal and a quick division sum will tell us the size of each exterior angle.

As an example we will find the exterior angle of a regular pentagon. We divide 360° by 5 to get 72°, the size of the exterior angle.

Interior Angles

An interior angle and its exterior angle add up to 180° because they are adjacent to one another on a straight line.
Thus for the regular pentagon an interior angle has size 180 - 72 = 108°.

Sum of interior angles

To find the sum of the interior angles simply ask yourself how many there are. In the regular pentagon, there are 5 interior angles each of 108°.
Thus the sum of the interior angles is 5 x 108 = 540°.

Interior and Exterior Angles

An alternative method - splitting into triangles

Starting at one <u>vertex</u> it is possible to draw two <u>diagonals</u> to split the pentagon into three triangles. Each triangle holds 180°. Thus 3 x 180 = 540° is the sum of the interior angles of all the triangles and also of the regular pentagon.

The number of triangles is always 2 less than the number of sides, so we can derive the following formulae for a <u>regular</u> n-sided <u>polygon</u>:

Sum of interior angles = 180(n-2)   **Interior angle = $\dfrac{180(n-2)}{n}$**

Exterior angle = $\dfrac{360}{n}$ or $180 - \dfrac{180(n-2)}{n}$

An alternative method - splitting into isosceles triangles

Split the centre into five angles of 72° forming five isosceles triangles. This enables you to work out the other two angles in each triangle.

Hence you can work out each interior angle.

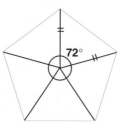

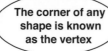

The corner of any shape is known as the vertex

Direction (which way to point) is given either by a compass point or by a three-figure bearing.

Main Compass Points

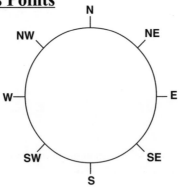

Bearings

Bearings are always measured <u>clockwise</u> from North.

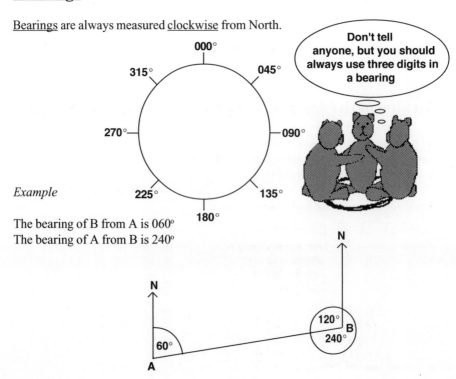

Don't tell anyone, but you should always use three digits in a bearing

Example

The bearing of B from A is 060º
The bearing of A from B is 240º

Logo Commands

Logo Commands

67

Logo is a programming language used to control a turtle's movement on a drawing screen. It is useful to help you understand angles, particularly exterior angles of polygons. There are different versions of Logo, so there may be some alternative commands in your version.

To start with, the turtle only understands a few words, like:

FORWARD	FD	FD 60
BACKWARD	BK	BK 42
RIGHT	RT	RT 90
LEFT	LT	LT 270
CLEAN	CL	
CLEAR SCREEN	CS	
LIFT		
DROP		
RUBBER		
SETPC		SETPC 5 — *This sets the pen colour*
SHOWTURTLE	ST	
HIDETURTLE	HT	
REPEAT		REPEAT 5 [FD 40 RT 90]

Then you can teach the turtle new words:

BUILD	BUILD SQUARE
OR	
TO	TO SQUARE
EDIT	EDIT SQUARE

To use a variable **BUILD SQUARE :SIDE** and use **FD :SIDE** in the procedure.

Circles

Pi or π

Pi is a number and is the <u>ratio</u> of the <u>circumference</u> of a circle to its <u>diameter</u>.
Its value is 3.14159 26535 89793 23846 ..... but either use calculator π or 3.14.

In the past, the fraction 22/7 was used as an approximation but in fact π cannot be written as a fraction.

Some Important Formulae

Circumference = π × diameter $C = \pi d$ $d = \dfrac{C}{\pi}$

Circumference = 2π × radius $C = 2\pi r$ $r = \dfrac{C}{2\pi}$

Area = π × radius × radius $A = \pi r^2$ $r = \sqrt{\dfrac{A}{\pi}}$

Example A

Find the area and circumference of a circle of radius 5 cm

Circumference = 2π × radius = 2π × 5 = 31.4 cm

Area = π × radius × radius = πr^2 = π × 5 × 5 = 25π = 78.5 cm^2

Example B

Find the dimensions of a square equal to the area of this semi-circle

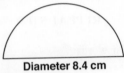

Diameter 8.4 cm

Radius = ½ Diameter = ½ × 8.4 = 4.2 cm

Area of semi-circle = ½π × radius × radius = ½πr^2 = ½π × 4.2 × 4.2 = 27.7 cm^2

Area of square = 27.7 cm^2

so side of square = $\sqrt{27.7}$ = 5.26 cm

Pythagoras' Theorem

Pythagoras' Theorem concerns the areas of squares placed on the three edges of a right-angled triangle.

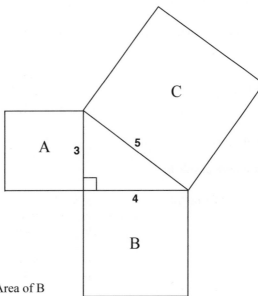

Area of C = Area of A + Area of B
i.e. $5^2 = 3^2 + 4^2$
         $25 = 9 + 16$

Pythagoras' Theorem says that **the area of the square on the hypotenuse of a right-angled triangle is equal to the sum of the areas of the squares on the other two shorter sides.**

In short: $a^2 + b^2 = c^2$

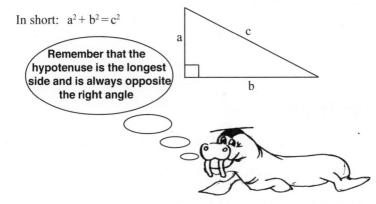

Remember that the hypotenuse is the longest side and is always opposite the right angle

Pythagoras' Theorem

Example A

Find the length of side a

By Pythagoras' Theorem:

$$a^2 = 5^2 + 12^2$$
$$= 25 + 144$$
$$= 169$$
$$a = \sqrt{169}$$
$$a = 13$$

Example B

Find the length of side b

By Pythagoras' Theorem:

$$b^2 + 24^2 = 25^2$$
$$b^2 + 576 = 625$$
$$b^2 = 49$$
$$b = \sqrt{49}$$
$$b = 7$$

Example C

Find the length AD

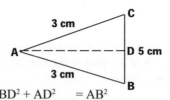

Note that BD = ½BC = 2.5 cm

By Pythagoras' Theorem in △ABD:

$$BD^2 + AD^2 = AB^2$$
$$2.5^2 + AD^2 = 3^2$$
$$6.25 + AD^2 = 9$$
$$AD^2 = 9 - 6.25 = 2.75$$
$$AD = \sqrt{2.75} = 1.66 \text{ cm}$$

Pythagorean Triads

These are whole numbered right-angled triangles and should be learned:

3, 4, 5   5, 12, 13   7, 24, 25   8, 15, 17   9, 40, 41

Multiples of these such as 6, 8, 10 or 50, 120, 130 may also be found.

Averages: The Mean

The <u>average</u> of a list of numbers is the value which can be used to represent the whole list. There are several types of average.

The <u>mean</u> is one type and is found by adding up all the numbers and dividing this total by how many numbers you added together.

Examples

The mean of 6, 8, 9, 2, 10 is $\dfrac{6 + 8 + 9 + 2 + 10}{5} = \dfrac{35}{5} = 7$

The mean of 3, 8, 12, 10 is $\dfrac{3 + 8 + 12 + 10}{4} = \dfrac{33}{4} = 8.25$

Sometimes we know the mean and how many numbers we have. In this case we can work out the total by multiplying the mean by the number of numbers.

Example A

If the mean of 5 numbers is 12, then their total must be $5 \times 12 = 60$.

Example B

If x, 6, 8, 10 have a mean of 9 then their total must be $9 \times 4 = 36$.

so $x + 6 + 8 + 10 = 36$

so $x = 12$

If there is a nought in your list of numbers, it must still be included

Averages: The Mean

To find the mean of a list of measured items, make sure that they are in the same unit of measurement throughout.

Example A

Find the mean length of 4 wooden planks measuring: 64cm, 1.3m, 4m and 3½m.

Find the total in cm: $64 + 130 + 400 + 350 = 944$

Then divide as usual: $944 \div 4 = 236$

Write in correct units: 236 cm or 2.36 m

Example B

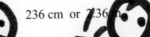

Find the average age of children of ages: 11yrs, 10yrs 7mths, 10yrs 9mths and 11yrs 4 mths.

With non-metric measurements, care is needed, especially with division.

Find the total in columns:

Keep years and months separate.

	Years	Months
	11	0
	10	7
	10	9
	11	4
Total:	42	20

Divide:

$$\begin{array}{c|cc} & 40 & 44 \\ 4 & 42 & 20 \\ & 10 & 11 \end{array}$$

carry 2 years over i.e. 24 months

Answer: 10 years 11 months

Range

It is simple to work out the range of a list of numbers. Simply subtract the smallest from the largest.

Example: The range of 3, 6, 5, 8, 11, 7, 4 is 8 because 11 - 3 = 8.

Mode

The <u>mode</u> is the most frequently occuring number in a list.

Example

In a <u>survey</u> of the number of children per family, the following results were obtained: 2, 2, 3, 2, 4, 3, 1, 0, 1

The <u>mode</u> or <u>modal value</u> is 2 children because most families in this example have 2 children.

Median

The <u>median</u> is the middle value when the numbers are placed <u>in order.</u>

Example A   **In a survey of shoe sizes, the following results were obtained: 8, 7, 9, 8, 9, 6, 11. Find the median shoe size.**

Step 1   Place the numbers in order: 6, 7, 8, 8, 9, 9, 11

Step 2   The median size is **8** because it is in the middle   **middle number**

Example B   **In a survey of sweet prices, the following results were obtained: 23p, 25p, 22p, 25p. Find the median price.**

Step 1   Place the numbers in order: 22, 23, 25, 25   **middle numbers**

Step 2   Find the mean of the middle numbers i.e. $\dfrac{23 + 25}{2} = 24$

The median price is **24p.**

Statistics

Pictograms

In a <u>pictogram</u> a symbol stands for a group of items.

Pictogram showing results of food survey

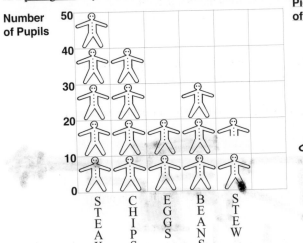

Number of Pupils

I stand for 10 people

Bar Charts or Column Graphs or Block Graphs

A Bar Chart is similar to a pictogram, but uses <u>rectangles</u> instead of pictures.

Use a <u>bar chart</u> when you are dealing with chunks of information.

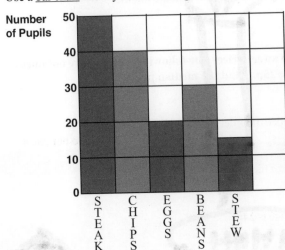

Number of Pupils

Bar Chart showing results of food survey

Pie Charts

Use a pie chart when your survey is about splitting something into smaller parts
eg how you spend your day, or how you spend a £12 present.

Example   **I spend £12 as follows: £5   Cassette**
                                      £1   Sweets
                                      £4   Lunch
                                      £2   Book

Show this information on a Pie Chart.

Step 1   Divide 360° by total: $360 \div 12 = \mathbf{30}$
Step 2   Multiply each quantity by   Cassette   **30** x 5 = 150°
                this figure to change to   Sweets   **30** x 1 = 30°
                degrees: Lunch   **30** x 4 = 120°
                                                 Book   **30** x 2 = 60°
Step 3   Draw the pie chart with these angles.

Step 4   Label each segment with its angle and title. Title the pie chart.

**Pie Chart showing
how £12 was spent**

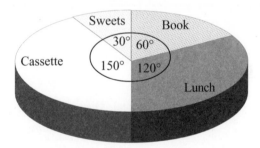

Line Graphs

Use a line graph to display continuous information eg temperature.
Make sure you take care with the scales on each axis.

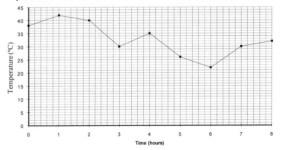

**Greenhouse
temperatures**

Conversion Graphs

Example   **Draw a conversion graph to convert pounds to French francs (£1=10FF)**

Step 1   Choose suitable scales and label axes.
Step 2   Plot two points as far apart as possible.

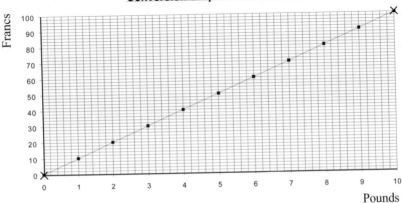

Conversion Graph: Pounds to Francs

Travel Graphs

Time always goes along the <u>horizontal</u>. Distance from a place goes on the <u>vertical</u>.

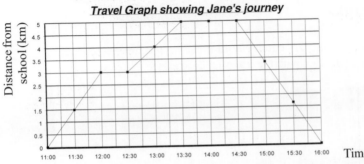

Travel Graph showing Jane's journey

The graph shows that Jane started walking at 3 km/h, had a 30 mins rest at noon and then continued at 2 km/h before having a 1 hour stop for lunch at 13:30. She then came straight to school, arriving back at 16:00.

Statistics

Scatter Graphs

Example **Draw a scatter graph to show the following data about shoe sizes and height.**

Step 1 Choose suitable scales and label axes.
Step 2 Plot points using crosses as coordinate pairs
Step 3 To draw the <u>line of best fit</u>, imagine the crosses as ducks on a river. Then, using a ruler, simply draw the centre line of the river.

Shoe Size	Height (cm)
3	145
6	154
8	171
5	150
7	166
8	168
9	175
5	155
9	173
4	150

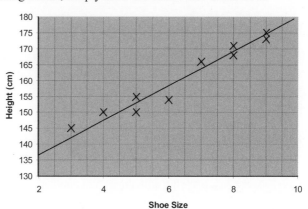

Correlation

Correlation is the connection between two variables. It can be <u>positive</u>, <u>negative</u>, or there can be no correlation. The line of best fit is a good indicator of the type of correlation. If there is no obvious line of best fit, then there is <u>no correlation</u>.

Positive	Negative	None

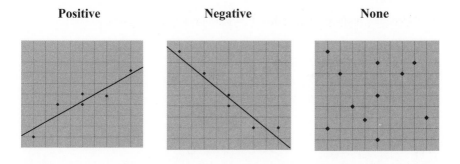

Probability

<u>Probability</u> is a measure of how likely an event is to occur.

The range is from   0   ⇨   1

will never
happen

will always
happen

To calculate probability we calculate this fraction:

<u>No. of ways your event can happen</u>
Total no. of possible outcomes

Example A

P(getting an even no. on a die) $= \dfrac{3}{6} = \dfrac{1}{2}$

This is because 2, 4, 6 are the only three even numbers out of six possibilities.

Example B

P(getting an ace from a pack of cards) $= \dfrac{4}{52} = \dfrac{1}{13}$

This is because there are 4 aces out of 52 possible cards in a pack.

Operations

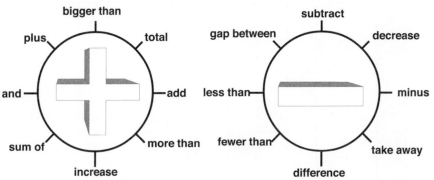

bigger than

plus — total

and — add

sum of — more than

increase

---

subtract

gap between — decrease

less than — minus

fewer than — take away

difference

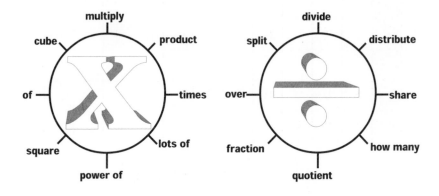

multiply

cube — product

of — times

square — lots of

power of

---

divide

split — distribute

over — share

fraction — how many

quotient

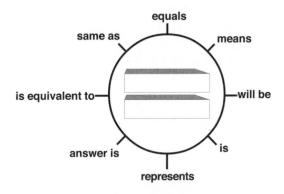

equals

same as — means

is equivalent to — will be

answer is — is

represents

Tables

✕	1	2	3	4	5	6	7	8	9	10	11	12
1	1	2	3	4	5	6	7	8	9	10	11	12
2	2	4	6	8	10	12	14	16	18	20	22	24
3	3	6	9	12	15	18	21	24	27	30	33	36
4	4	8	12	16	20	24	28	32	36	40	44	48
5	5	10	15	20	25	30	35	40	45	50	55	60
6	6	12	18	24	30	36	42	48	54	60	66	72
7	7	14	21	28	35	42	49	56	63	70	77	84
8	8	16	24	32	40	48	56	64	72	80	88	96
9	9	18	27	36	45	54	63	72	81	90	99	108
10	10	20	30	40	50	60	70	80	90	100	110	120
11	11	22	33	44	55	66	77	88	99	110	121	132
12	12	24	36	48	60	72	84	96	108	120	132	144

Learn these tables

There are not very many tables which have to be learnt.
Excluding the 1s, 2s, 10s and most of the 11s we are left with just 38 tables to learn:

3 x 3	4 x 4	5 x 5	6 x 6	7 x 7	8 x 8	9 x 9	11 x 11	12 x 12
3 x 4	4 x 5	5 x 6	6 x 7	7 x 8	8 x 9	9 x 12	11 x 12	
3 x 5	4 x 6	5 x 7	6 x 8	7 x 9	8 x 12			
3 x 6	4 x 7	5 x 8	6 x 9	7 x 12				
3 x 7	4 x 8	5 x 9	6 x 12					
3 x 8	4 x 9	5 x 12						
3 x 9	4 x 12							
3 x 12								

INDEX

En
con
mi/mis

¿CÓMO?

¿ Dónde ?

A donde
¿que?

Además
pero